Christmas

Five Festive Poems for Children

ex libris

Candlestick Press

Published by:
Candlestick Press,
Diversity House, 72 Nottingham Road, Arnold, Nottingham UK NG5 6LF
www.candlestickpress.co.uk

Design and typesetting by Diversity Creative Marketing Solutions Ltd.,
www.diversity.agency

Printed by Ratcliff & Roper Print Group, Nottinghamshire, UK

Donation to UNICEF www.unicef.org.uk

ISBN 978 1 907598 57 9

Acknowledgements:

The poems in this pamphlet are reprinted from the following books, all by
permission of the publishers listed unless stated otherwise. Every effort has
been made to trace the copyright holders of the poems published in this
book. The editor and publisher apologise if any material has been included
without permission or without the appropriate acknowledgement, and
would be glad to be told of anyone who has not been consulted. Thanks are
due to all the copyright holders cited below for their kind permission:

Gabriel Fitzmaurice, *Splat & Other Great Poems* (Mercier Press, 2012) by
kind permission of the author

Walter de la Mare, *The Complete Poems of Walter de la Mare* (Faber &
Faber, 1973) out of copyright

John Mole, *The Wonder Dish* (OUP, 2002) by kind permission of
the author

Rachel Rooney, poem as yet unpublished, by kind permission of the author

George Szirtes, poem as yet unpublished, by kind permission of the author

All permissions cleared courtesy of Swift Permissions
(swiftpermissions@gmail.com)

Where poets are no longer living, their dates are given.

Santa Claus

Santa Claus is coming
To the village hall,
I'm going to see Santa Claus
And I won't cry at all.

Hello Santa! This is me!
(Oh Dad, he's awful hairy!
Oh Dad, don't let him near me!
Oh Dad, he's awful scary!).

Santa Claus was here today
In the village hall –
He gave me crisps and lemonade
(All I could do was bawl).

Gabriel Fitzmaurice

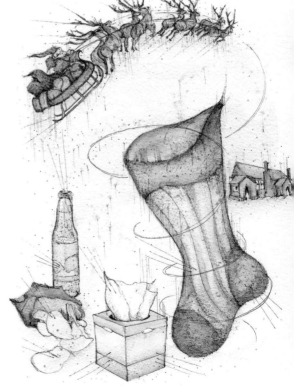

At the Pantomime

Yes, it was great to laugh
When one of the ugly sisters thought she was more beautiful
Than her other half,
And it was fun to cheer
When out of the magic lantern with a puff of smoke
We saw the genie appear,
And it was time to weep
When Snow White bit into the shiny apple
Or Beauty pricked her finger and fell asleep,
And it was really good
When the Prince arrived to wake them up
Though of course we knew that he would,
But best of all
When the villain sneaked on
(And, no, we didn't really want him to be gone)
It was absolute bliss
To hiss!

John Mole

Stocking

Superhero sticker book.
Eye patch and pirate hook.

Chocolate coin.

Bubble bath. Light-up socks.
Tintin money box.

Chocolate coin.

Don't know – check it later.
Maybe it's a calculator.

Chocolate coin.

Secret Mission spy set.
Look, I've got a virtual pet.

More chocolate coins.

Last lump. Shake some more.
Orange rolls out to the floor.

Tricked again. Never fear!
Won't be fooled next year.

Rachel Rooney

Mistletoe

Sitting under the mistletoe
(Pale-green, fairy mistletoe),
One last candle burning low,
All the sleepy dancers gone,
Just one candle burning on,
Shadows lurking everywhere:
Some one came, and kissed me there.

Tired I was; my head would go
Nodding under the mistletoe
(Pale-green, fairy mistletoe);
No footsteps came, no voice, but only,
Just as I sat there, sleepy, lonely,
Stooped in the still and shadowy air
Lips unseen – and kissed me there.

Walter de la Mare (1873 - 1956)

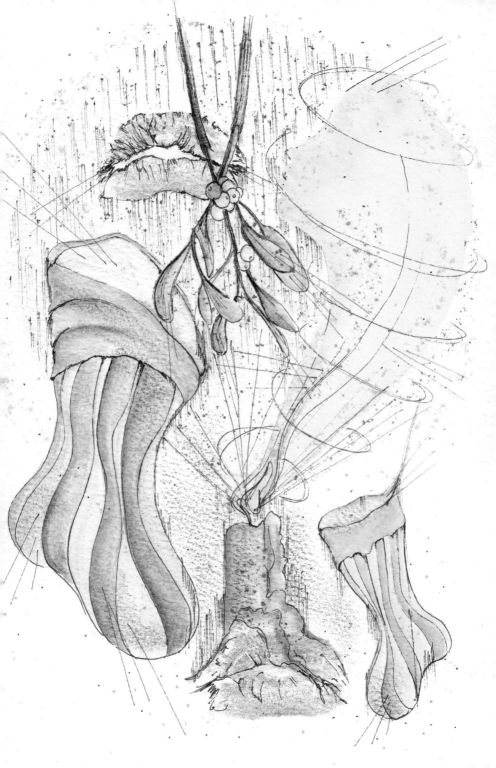

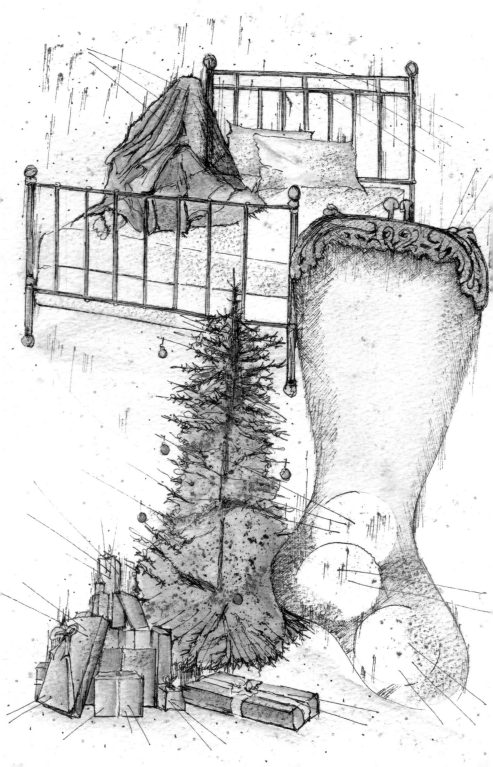

Night Excursion

When winter crawls into your bones
And sits up shivering in bed
The thought of shining winter gifts
Pops into its frozen head.

It puts on warm clothes and creeps down
Into the room where presents go.
Looks around, walks into town,
Despite the rain that might be snow,

Stopping at windows to look hard
To check what's better and what's worse,
And finds the perfect gift and card
Then fumbles in its icy purse

(Its pockets several miles deep)
For coins like moons, then doubles back
A pile of presents in its sack,
Slips into bed and falls asleep.

George Szirtes